THIS JOURNAL LOOKS ON THE BRIGHT SIDE

KNOCK KNOCK®
VENICE, CALIFORNIA

ABOUT THIS JOURNAL

THE SIX SECTIONS IN THIS JOURNAL ENCOMPASS A SPECTRUM OF GRATITUDE—AND HONESTY. FIND THE PROMPT THAT SPEAKS TO YOUR MOOD TODAY, THEN WRITE ABOUT IT.

WHAT I HAVE TO BE THANKFUL FOR
YEP, I'M GRATEFUL
BTW, THX!
GRATITUDE'S AN ATTITUDE
TODAY I HAVE TO SAY THANK YOU

HOW CAN I CHANGE MY OUTLOOK?
I'M GONNA STOP TAKING THIS FOR GRANTED
DON'T HATE, APPRECIATE
GRACIAS! MERCI! DANKE!
#SOBLESSED

WHAT'S BLISSING ME OUT
WHAT'S MAKING ME HAPPY
IT'S HAPPENING!
ELATION IS MY EMOTION
THRILLING THINGS I'M THINKING ABOUT
TODAY IS SUPER JOYFUL

CAN I GET A HALLELUJAH?
CRAZY-COOL ECSTATIC!
SITTING ON CLOUD NINE
HIP-HIP-HOORAY!
YES TO ALL THIS
AN ENCHANTED DAY

THINGS I WANT TO PONDER
HOW I AM GOING TO BE PRESENT
CONSIDERING MY BODY AND MIND
I DISCOVERED THIS ABOUT MYSELF
THOUGHTFUL THOUGHTS

JUST BREATHE
RECEPTIVE TO GOOD VIBES
HOW I ADDED TO MY GOOD KARMA
FOCUSING ON THE PRESENT
LETTING GO OF THE PAST

WHY I'M CONTENT TO BE CONTENT
WHAT'S GOING MY WAY TODAY
NO WORRIES
"PERFECT" IS THE ENEMY OF THE GOOD
HAPPY WITH MY PLACE IN THE UNIVERSE

SOME THINGS THAT WERE OKAY-ISH
THIS GAVE ME PEACE
IT'S ALL GOOD
FEELING FULFILLED
THIS WILL DO NICELY

WHY I'M GONNA LOOK ON THE BRIGHT SIDE
THE GLASS IS HALF FULL
WHY I'M WEARING ROSE-COLORED GLASSES
TODAY IS GOING TO BE A GOOD DAY
EVERYTHING'S COMING UP ME

CHEERFUL THOUGHTS
TODAY I WAS GOOD AT SOME THINGS
A FORTUITOUS SEQUENCE OF EVENTS
I GOT LUCKY TODAY
WOOHOO!

TODAY WASN'T REALLY SO HOT
EVERYONE IS ANNOYING
CAN'T COMPLAIN (BUT I COULD TRY)
THIS MADE ME AWFULLY UNCOMFORTABLE
REALLY, UNIVERSE?

YOU WON'T BELIEVE THIS
CANNOT CATCH A BREAK
KARMA BIT ME IN THE ASS TODAY
FRANKLY, I'M A LITTLE BEWILDERED
SHIT HAPPENS

GRATI TUDE

WHAT I HAVE TO
BE THANKFUL FOR

DATE: /   /

OKAY, OKAY, I'M GRATEFUL ALREADY!

YEP, I'M GRATEFUL

OKAY, OKAY, I'M GRATEFUL ALREADY!

BTW, THX!

GRATITUDE'S
AN ATTITUDE

DATE: /   /

DATE: / /

OKAY, OKAY, I'M GRATEFUL ALREADY!

TODAY I HAVE TO
SAY THANK YOU

OKAY, OKAY, I'M GRATEFUL ALREADY!

HOW CAN I CHANGE MY OUTLOOK?

DATE: / /

OKAY, OKAY, I'M GRATEFUL ALREADY!

I'M GONNA STOP TAKING
THIS FOR GRANTED

DATE: /   /

DATE: / /

OKAY, OKAY, I'M GRATEFUL ALREADY!

DON'T HATE, APPRECIATE

DATE: /   /

OKAY, OKAY, I'M GRATEFUL ALREADY!

GRACIAS! MERCI! DANKE!

OKAY, OKAY, I'M GRATEFUL ALREADY!

DATE: / /

OKAY, OKAY, I'M GRATEFUL ALREADY!

BLISS

WHAT'S BLISSING ME OUT

DATE: / /

ENJOYING EVERY MINUTE.

WHAT'S MAKING ME HAPPY

IT'S HAPPENING!

DATE: / /

ELATION IS MY EMOTION

THRILLING THINGS
I'M THINKING ABOUT

DATE: / /

DATE: /   /

ENJOYING EVERY MINUTE.

TODAY IS SUPER JOYFUL

DATE: /   /

ENJOYING EVERY MINUTE.

CAN I GET A HALLELUJAH?

CRAZY-COOL ECSTATIC!

DATE: /   /

ENJOYING EVERY MINUTE.

SITTING ON CLOUD NINE

DATE: /   /

ENJOYING EVERY MINUTE.

HIP-HIP-HOORAY!

DATE: /   /

YES TO ALL THIS

AN ENCHANTED DAY

MIND
FUL
NESS

THINGS I WANT TO PONDER

HOW I AM GOING TO BE PRESENT

DATE: / /

CONSIDERING MY BODY AND MIND

I DISCOVERED THIS
ABOUT MYSELF

DATE: / /

THOUGHTFUL THOUGHTS

DATE: /   /

JUST BREATHE

RECEPTIVE TO GOOD VIBES

DATE: /   /

HOW I ADDED TO
MY GOOD KARMA

TOP OF MIND.

FOCUSING ON THE PRESENT

LETTING GO OF THE PAST

CON TENT MENT

WHY I'M CONTENT
TO BE CONTENT

IT DOESN'T ALL HAVE TO BE FIREWORKS.

WHAT'S GOING
MY WAY TODAY

NO WORRIES

SOME THINGS THAT WERE OKAY-ISH

DATE: /   /

IT DOESN'T ALL HAVE TO BE FIREWORKS.

FEELING FULFILLED

IT DOESN'T ALL HAVE TO BE FIREWORKS.

DATE: /   /

OPTIMISM

WHY I'M GONNA LOOK ON THE BRIGHT SIDE

DATE: / /

TURN MY FROWN UPSIDE DOWN.

WHY I'M WEARING ROSE-COLORED GLASSES

TURN MY FROWN UPSIDE DOWN.

TODAY IS GOING TO BE A GOOD DAY

DATE: / /

EVERYTHING'S COMING UP ME

DATE: / /

TURN MY FROWN UPSIDE DOWN.

CHEERFUL THOUGHTS

TURN MY FROWN UPSIDE DOWN.

TODAY I WAS GOOD
AT SOME THINGS

DATE: / /

TURN MY FROWN UPSIDE DOWN.

A FORTUITOUS
SEQUENCE OF EVENTS

DATE: / /

TURN MY FROWN UPSIDE DOWN.

I GOT LUCKY TODAY

DATE: / /

DATE: /   /

TURN MY FROWN UPSIDE DOWN.

WOOHOO!

DATE: / /

TURN MY FROWN UPSIDE DOWN.

REALITY

TODAY WASN'T REALLY SO HOT

CAN'T COMPLAIN
(BUT I COULD TRY)

THIS MADE ME AWFULLY UNCOMFORTABLE

DATE: / /

CANNOT CATCH A BREAK

DATE: / /

FRANKLY, I'M A
LITTLE BEWILDERED

SHIT HAPPENS

Created, published, and distributed by Knock Knock
1635 Electric Ave.
Venice, CA 90291
knockknockstuff.com
Knock Knock is a registered trademark of Knock Knock LLC

This book is meant solely for entertainment purposes. In no event will Knock Knock be liable
to any reader for any harm, injury, or damages, including direct, indirect, incidental, special,
consequential, or punitive arising out of or in connection with the use of the information
contained in this book. So there.

ISBN: 978-168349086-9
UPC: 825703-50242-8

10 9 8 7 6 5 4 3